The Hungry Donkey

Heather Amery

Illustrated by Stephen Cartwright

Language consultant: Betty Root
Series editor: Jenny Tyler

How to use this book

This book tells a story about the Boot family who live on Apple Tree Farm.
Some words in the story have been replaced by pictures.
Find the stickers that match these pictures and stick them over the top.
Each sticker has the word with it to help you read the story.

Some of the big pictures have pieces missing.
Find the stickers with the missing pieces to finish the pictures.

A yellow duck is hidden in every picture. When you have found
the duck you can put a 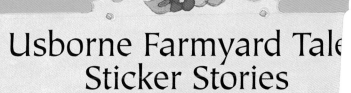 sticker on the page.

This is Apple Tree Farm.

Mrs. Boot, the farmer, lives on Apple Tree Farm.

She has two
children
called Poppy and Sam.

She also has a
dog
called Rusty.

There is a donkey on the farm.

The donkey is called Ears.

She lives in a field with lots of 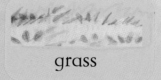grass,

but she is always hungry.

Ears the donkey is going out on a trip.

Sam and  (Poppy) catch  (Ears)

and take her to the farmyard. Today is the day

of the village show.

4

They brush her coat and clean her feet.

They comb her  tail too. Ears has a little

 cart . They strap her to her

little cart ready for the show.

They all go down the lane.

Poppy and Sam ride in the  cart .

As usual,  Ears is feeling

very hungry.

6

Poppy and Sam jump down from the cart.

 Mrs. Boot ties Ears to a  fence .

"Stay here, Ears. We'll be back soon when it's time

for the best donkey competition," says Sam.

Ears is hungry and bored.

She has nothing to do. Ears pulls and pulls on the rope until she is free.

She wanders off to see what she can find.

Ears looks for food.

She trots across the field to the show ring.

She sees a bunch of  flowers and some

 fruit . "Those look tasty," she thinks.

Ears takes a big bite.

A lady with  and a blue

glasses

flowery dress screams loudly. Lots of

look at Ears.

10

people

Ears is frightened and runs away.

Mrs. Boot, Poppy, Sam and the  lady

run after her and catch her.

"Naughty donkey," says  Sam .

Ears is in disgrace.

"I'm very sorry," says  to the lady.

Mrs. Boot

"Would you like to take  into the

Ears

best donkey competition?"

12

I found the duck!

I found the duck!

I found the duck!

I found the duck!

rosette

people

I found the duck!

I found the duck!

I found the duck!

I found the duck!

I found the duck!

I found the duck!

I found the duck!

Mrs. Rose

I found the duck!

I found the duck!

hat

I found the duck!

I found the duck!

hat

I found the duck!

The lady's name is Mrs. Rose.

 helps her to climb into the cart.

Poppy

"Come along, Ears," says  .

Mrs. Rose

Ears behaves very well now.

13

Ears trots into the ring.

All the  are watching.

She trots around the ring, pulling the cart.

She stops and goes when  tells her.

14

Ears behaves so well that she wins a prize.

"Very good," says the judge and gives her a

. He gives Mrs. Rose a prize too.

It's a lovely new  .

Mrs. Rose waves goodbye.

"That was such fun," she says. Ears trots

home. Now Ears has a  too!

Cover design by Vici Leyhane   Digital manipulation by Nelupa Hussain

This edition first published in 2004 by Usborne Publishing Ltd, Usborne House, 83-85 Saffron Hill, London EC1N 8RT, England. www.usborne.com